This book belongs to:

. . . .

. . . .

An Hachette UK Company
www.hachette.co.uk

First published in France in 2013 by Dessain et Tolra

This edition published in Great Britain in 2015 by
Hamlyn, a division of Octopus Publishing Group Ltd
Carmelite House
50 Victoria Embankment
London EC4Y 0DZ
www.octopusbooks.co.uk

ISBN 978-0-600-63242-9

A CIP catalogue record for this book is available from the British Library.

Printed and bound in China

10 9 8

Editorial directors: Isabelle Jeuge-Maynart and Ghislaine Stora
Layout and cover: Claire Morel Fatio
Translation: JMS Books LLP (www.jmswords.com)
Assistant Production Manager: Caroline Alberti

Colouring for mindfulness

ZEN

50 mandalas to help you de-stress

hamlyn

How to stay Zen with mandalas

The mandala is a part of Hindu tradition. It is a semi-abstract, semi-figurative design that aids meditation. Restful and relaxing, it opens the way to inner calm and letting go. It is relatively symmetrical in structure, with different kinds of geometric motifs surrounding a well-defined centre. The mandala is always enclosed by an outer border, while the eye is immediately drawn towards the central point.

There are different ways of 'working' with mandalas: colouring in, drawing, contemplation.

This book contains 50 mandalas to colour in. Just choose one that appeals to you instinctively, at random, and begin. There are no rules: use whatever medium you like – felt tips, pencils, gouache, pastels – and whatever colours you like from the selection available. A feeling of calm will gradually take over and you will be completely absorbed in what you are doing and the colours filling up the blank shapes. It's a great way to simply let go of everyday cares!

You can also design your own mandalas. Draw the concentric circles and radiating lines freehand or with the help of a compass and ruler. See what shapes and motifs emerge from your pencil as you work your way towards the centre. Don't plan, just see what happens. Six of the mandalas in this book have been left unfinished for you to complete, in whatever direction your imagination takes you.

Contemplating a mandala encourages concentration and meditation. Once you have coloured them in, cut out one or two of the mandalas that inspire you the most. Display them in a peaceful environment and contemplate them, allowing your thoughts to run free. Little by little, you will begin to relax and feel peaceful and rested.

Always have a mandala close at hand to colour in - between 5 and 10 minutes a day should be enough to recharge your batteries.

Complete this mandala in whatever way you wish and give free rein to your imagination...

Complete this mandala with other concentric shapes and geometric motifs.
Use a compass and a ruler if necessary.

Draw along the dotted lines and extend them, working
towards the centre in whatever way you wish.

Extend the lines and geometric shapes however you wish.

Extend the lines and geometric shapes however you wish.

Extend the lines and geometric shapes however you wish.